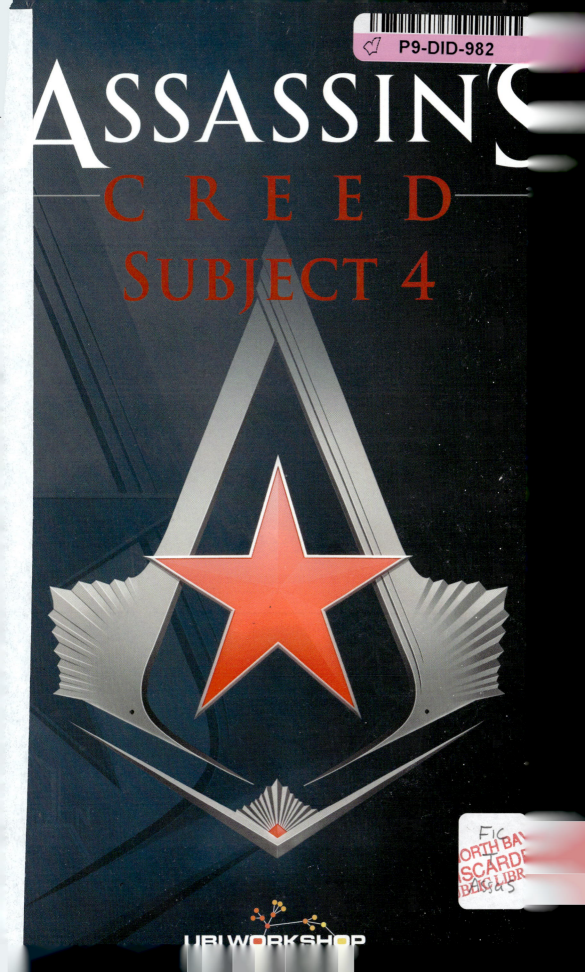

ASSASSIN'S
CREED
SUBJECT 4

UBI WORKSHOP

ASSASSIN'S CREED ®

WRITTEN BY

Karl Kerschl & Cameron Stewart

ART BY

Karl Kerschl & Cameron Stewart

COLOUR ART BY

Nadine Thomas & Tyson Hesse

WITH Joël Séguin - Blond - Ian Herring

DIRECTED AND LETTERED BY

Studio Lounak's Serge LaPointe

UBI WORKSHOP

EXECUTIVE PRODUCER
SÉBASTIEN PUEL

PRODUCER
JULIEN CUNY

UNIVERSE ADVISORS
JEAN GUESDON, COREY MAY & STÉPHANE BLAIS

ASSASSIN'S CREED SUBJECT 4, 2012. First Printing.

Maquette and Graphic Design by Studio Lounak

Published by:
Ubi Workshop Inc, 5000-5505 boul. St-Laurent,
Montréal (Québec), H2T 1S6 - Canada.

ISBN 978-2-924006-06-1
PRINTED IN CANADA

CHAPTER
ONE

THE FALL

OCTOBER 15, 1888

FOR THE EYES OF NIKOLAI ORELOV. OF UTMOST URGENCY. DESTROY IMMEDIATELY AFTER READING.

OUR BROTHERS IN THE ROYAL HOUSE HAVE INFORMED US THAT THE TSAR ALEXANDER III WILL BE RETURNING TO ST. PETERSBURG FROM A FAMILY RETREAT IN CRIMEA ON OCTOBER 17.

THE BROTHERHOOD'S SUCCESS WITH THE REMOVAL OF THE PREVIOUS TSAR DID MUCH TO PREVENT FURTHER TEMPLAR CONTROL OF RUSSIA AND THE NEIGHBOURING REGIONS.

THOUGH IT MAY NOT BE EVIDENT TO THE SHORT-SIGHTED, THE MENTOR PREDICTS THAT WESTERN EUROPE IS APPROACHING A CRITICAL JUNCTION. THE TSAR'S CURRENT DIRECTION GIVES US REASON TO BELIEVE THAT THE RUSSIAN AUTOCRACY WILL BE STRENGTHENED RATHER THAN TEMPERED, AS WE HAD HOPED.

DDABUMP BUDDABUMP BUDDABUMP

PHWEEEEEE

AS SUCH, WE CAN WASTE NO TIME IN PLAYING OUR HAND.

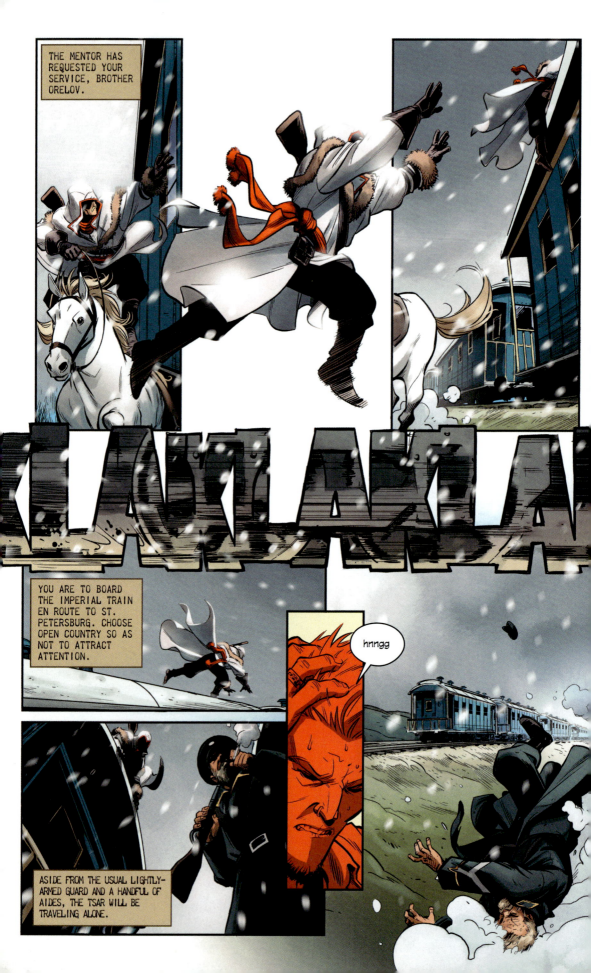

CHK-K

...that...

Mother?

AAAAAAA

You dare...

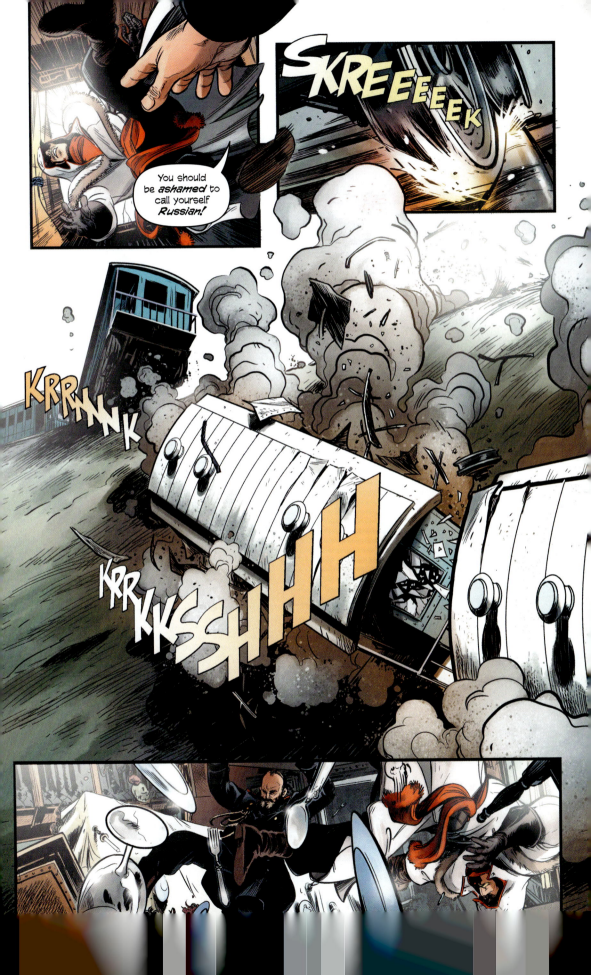

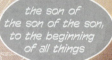

Eden

the son of the son of the son, to the beginning of all things

Make yourself *useful*, Nikolai. A useless thing has no value.

I am not you

Welcome to the Brotherhood

remember whe we went wal in the woo

Don't you see? The memories exist at all times and in all places at once. We can access them, but to build an accurate timeline... I don't think it's possible.

ll of e trees that year?

I can't feel mysel breathi

Or maybe it's that I can feel *everything* breathing

A single, infinitely complex organism

Destroyed...

It is destroyed...

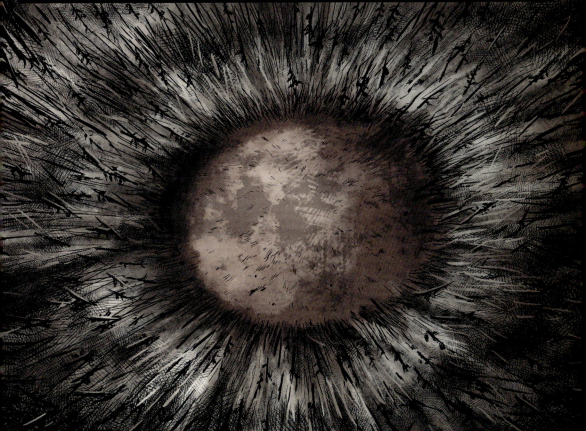

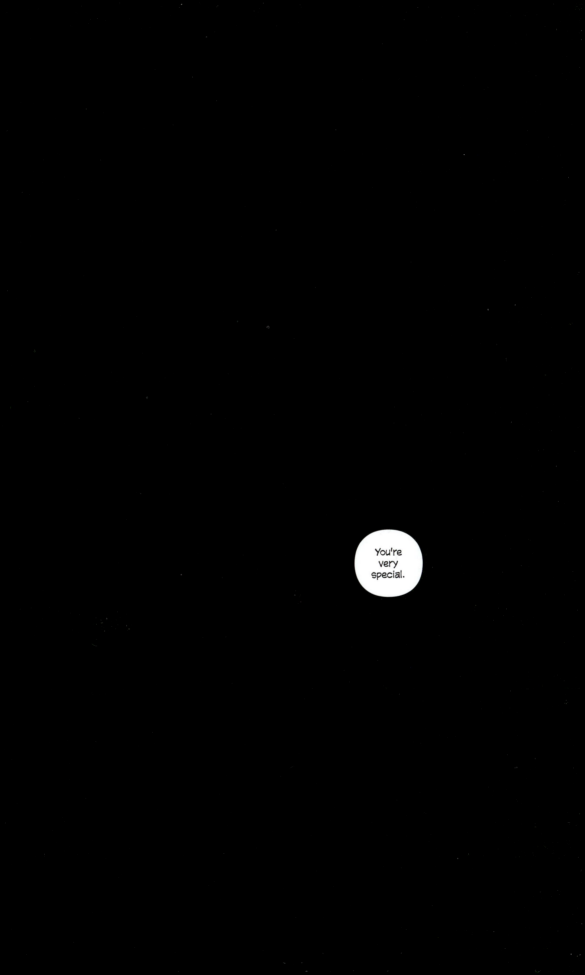

Dear Nikolai Andreievich,

Forgive me for my poor habits of correspondence.

An unfortunate side effect of fraternal ties is that one begins to feel comfortable taking one's brother for granted.

And, indeed, though we are not bound by blood, can we not consider each other as family?

My own brother, Aleksandr, was as important an example to me as any man could have, and you were always there by his side, so you will forgive the informality of kinship that I feel (and have always felt) toward you.

The Revolution has begun!

A revolution you (and he) helped start is now spreading across Russia; an inevitable force whose time has finally come.
This is but the first wave of change. Soon, very soon, power will shift to the hands of the proletariat, and we will finally see real progress in our country.

Imagine, Nikolai, what your father would say were he to see this day.

I write to you from Zurich, but I am making preparations to return to Petrograd, where I intend to construct a new Socialist order. And this is the purpose of my letter, brother.

Although the Tsar has abdicated the throne, he and his family remain a threat to all we have built - a living banner of a dead ruling class.

I know that your responsibilities are delegated from within your Order, and while the Brotherhood may no longer consider Nicholas a threat, I appeal to your sense of justice and national pride.

Dispose of this last symbol of Imperialism, once and for all, and let us be done with it! The Royal family will have been moved from the palace and will no doubt be waiting on word from England for asylum. I urge you to act before they are permitted to leave the country.

The future of Russia depends on you. I will contact you upon my arrival to congratulate your success in person.

Regards to your family, Nikolai.
Yours always,
V.I Lenin

The Revolution has begun!

A revolution you (and he) helped start is now spreading across Russia; an inevitable force whose time has finally come.
This is but the first wave of change. Soon, very soon, power will shift to the hands of the proletariat, and we will finally see real progress in our country.

Imagine, Nikolai, what your father would say were he to see this day.

I write to you from Zurich, but I am making preparations to return to Petrograd, where I intend to construct a new Socialist order. And this is the purpose of my letter, brother.

Although the Tsar has abdicated the throne, he and his family remain a threat to all we have built – a living banner of a dead ruling class.

I know that your responsibilities are delegated from within your Order, and while the Brotherhood may no longer consider Nicholas a threat, I appeal to your sense of justice and national pride.

Dispose of this last symbol of Imperialism, once and for all, and let us be done with it! The Royal family will have been moved from the palace and will no doubt be waiting on word from England for asylum. I urge you to act before they are permitted to leave the country.

The future of Russia depends on you. I will contact you upon my arrival to congratulate your success in person.

Regards to your family, Nikolai.
Yours always,
V.I Lenin

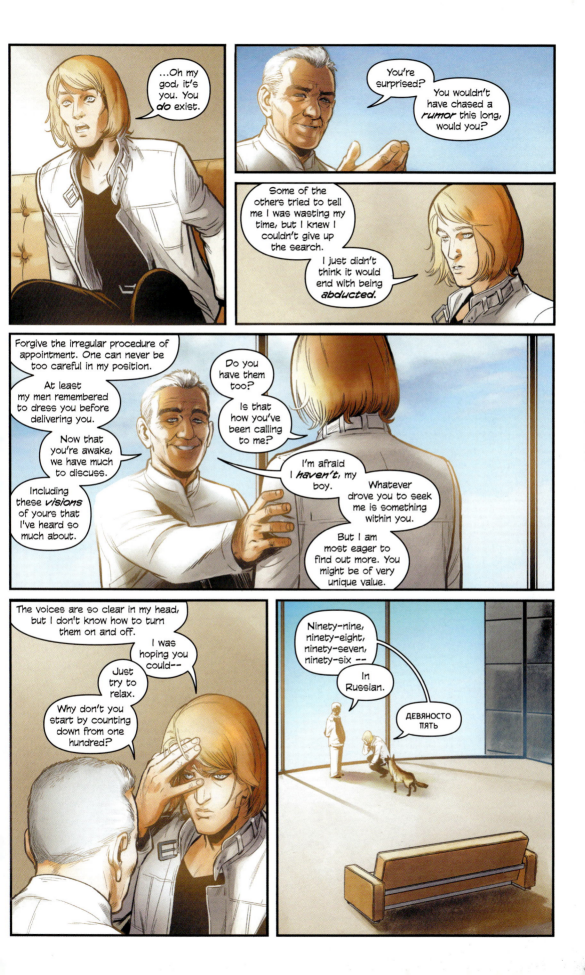

From: Vidic, Warren
To: Rikkin, Alan
CC: Kilkerman, David
Nilop, Nancy
Subject: Homecoming

As you may already be aware, Animus Project Subject 4, code-name Daniel Cross, has at long last returned to our Philadelphia research Facility.

I am pleased to report that despite the many years that have passed since we released him into the wild, Cross followed his programming precisely and unwittingly, and after successful infiltration was able to eliminate the strategic command of the Assassin Order.

With the information retrieved from Cross, we now may mobilize tactical teams to initiate strikes on Assassin compounds globally.

whiiiiiiine

We have turned over a rock and sent the insects scurrying, but we will stamp on them before they can hide again. I am confident that we will soon witness the fall of the Order of Assassins, and we may fulfill our ambitions unimpeded.

How could we --he was supposed to help us--

Move, people, MOVE!

We have to evacuate immediately!

That bastard's been to every training camp we have, all over the world! They know where we are!

I admit I felt a certain sense of almost fatherly pride, seeing our boy grown and carrying on our work.

Indeed, any lingering attachment to his deceased parents has dissolved and he has come to regard Abstergo as his home.

Despite this, Cross was extremely agitated upon his return and made several insistent requests to be returned to the Animus device.

An attack on an unfortunate secretary convinced us of his urgency.

Inserting him into the device proved to have a calming effect and it is my recommendation that he remain connected for the time being.

He is with his family now.

CHAPTER
ONE

EPILOGUE

Location confirmed. Entry Team go.

Move! Move! Move!

LAUNDR

Sweep the AO. You're looking for a lock, some kind of *entrance*...

Here!

Combination lock, 9-digit numeric code.

Go ahead.

354 67-

ACCESS GRANTE

BLEEP

BRAKK

BAM

P-please... we have children here...

BRAKK

For Assassins, they're not putting up much of a --

RAAAAAA

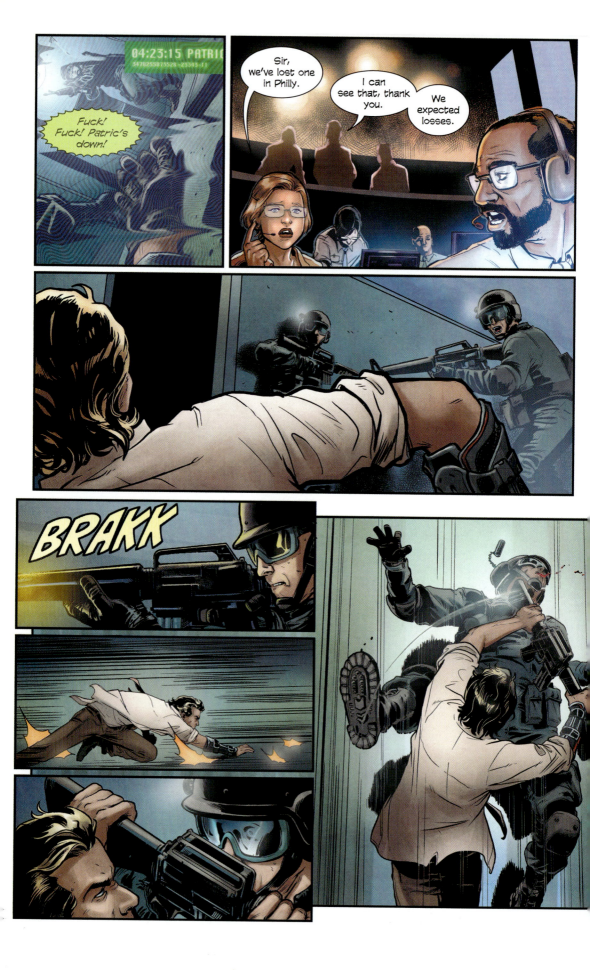

WHUD

Okay now, take it easy--

Templar scum, you won't--

BLAM BLAM BLAM BLAM

We already *have.*

We've got a *dry hole* here.

Control, we have a problem.

We're coming up empty. Intel doesn't match up.

We're *missing* something.

Doctor Sung, are you hearing this?

We need further information.

Mr. Stearns, I don't know what you want me to do--

I've already administered as much of the SK-345 as his system can handle.

What is his condition?

He's holding stable, but he's exhausted.

We've been extracting information from him for almost 19 hours straight.

Hm.

Time is short. Increase the dosage.

I can't risk that!

He's a human being, he could die!

He is an asset of this corporation, doctor.

He is our property and we will decide how he is best used.

You, however, are merely an employee. As such, you can easily be *terminated*.

Sneaky fuckers.

KCHK CHK CHK CHK

Okay. Ready for entry.

Shhhfzzzzzzzzzzzzzzk

szzzzzk

We've lost the video feed, sir, they're too deep underground.

sssffzzzfound it.

Oh my god. We found it.

CHAPTER TWO

THE CHAIN

Hehn.

She's still alive?

She came this way.

Not for long.

Oh.

Come, *Kenya*. We follow. She won't be far.

The sooner you finish it the sooner we eat, eh?

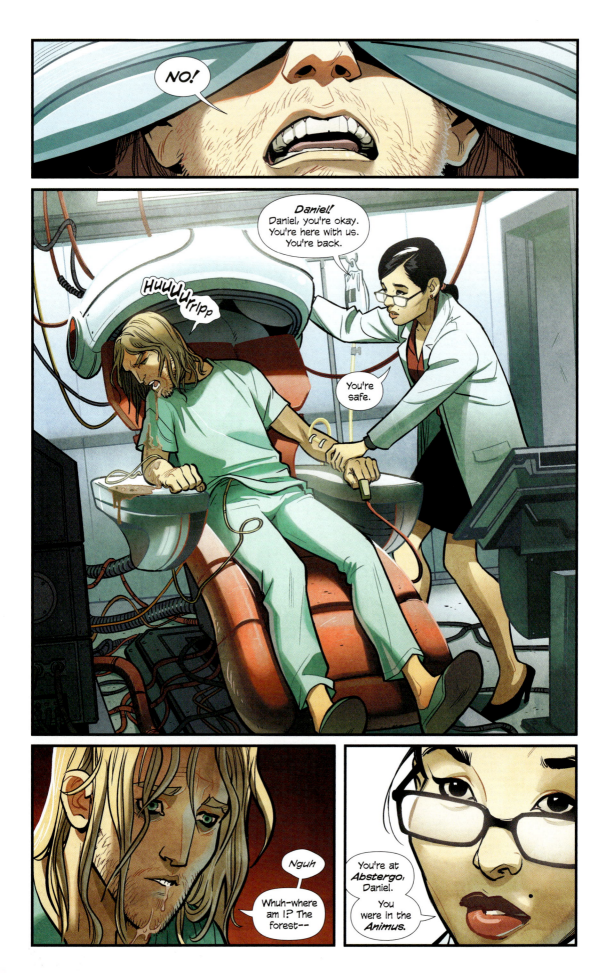

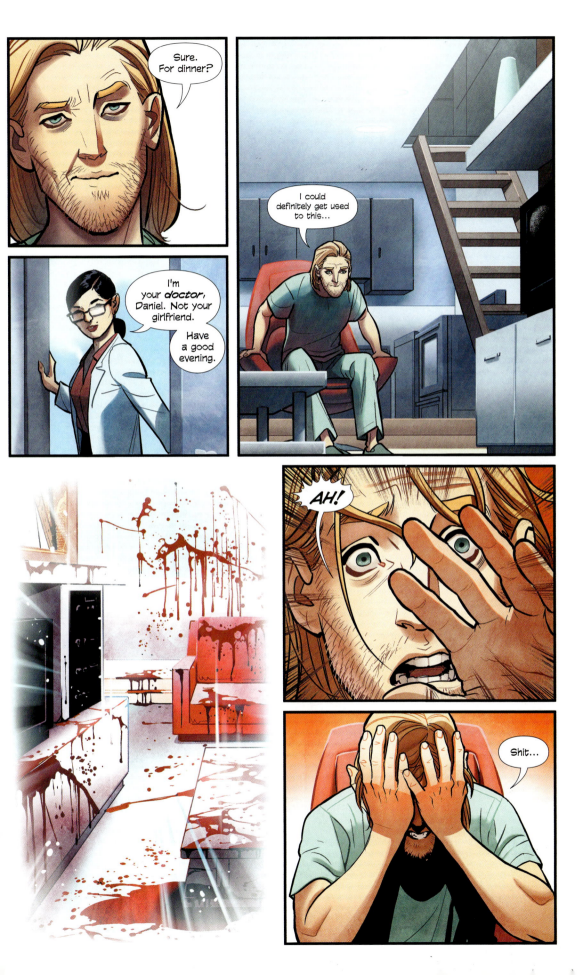

WHONGG

AAGH!

KLONGG

UTT--

HAACCHH

HAHH

Heeennhh

HACCHH

HKKKk--

HKK--

KK--

Hahh

Hahh

Hahh

БОЖЕ МОИ...

I had hoped to never see this day...

We must prepare ourselves, Kenya.

More men will be coming.

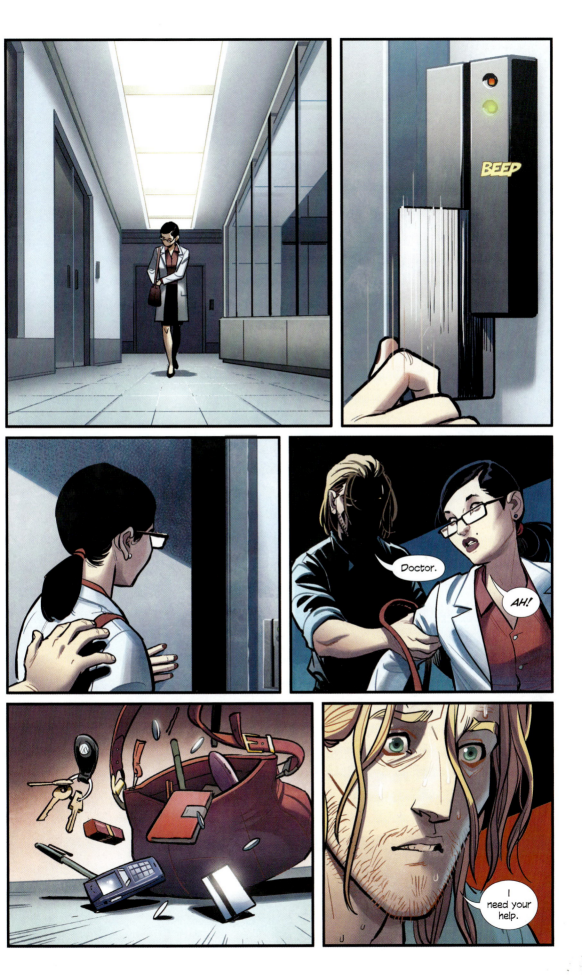

Look at you, all grown up...

Now, how does this thing work?

HA HA HA

Hello? Is someone there?

That

was

weird...

БУДЕМ ЗДОРОВЫ!

Come come, Nikolai, don't let good vodka go to waste!

Drink up!

I told you I did not wish to get drunk tonight, *Isak*.

Of course not, you wouldn't want to *enjoy* yourself, would you?

Tell me, whatever did your poor wife do to deserve such a humourless man?

Bravo, Nikolai! Workers of the world unite, eh?

Shortly after the raids, the prisoners were put on a ship bound for Finland; a curious destination, as they were then at war with Russia.

There were rumours that some prisoners were killed, shot by Finnish soldiers as they crossed the Russian border.

I cannot be sure that your mother and sister were among them, but in all this time I have not received word that they are alive...

I can only assume they are not.

That man today... the one you killed, is he the one who took mother and Nadya?

No, but he worked with those who did.

Many years ago I... took something from them, and now they are coming to take it back.

And when they come, will you kill them also?

No, Kenya...

...*you* will.

Now.
Come at me.

Papa...?

DO AS YOUR FATHER TELLS YOU, INNOKENTI!!

CHFF

This is how you approach an enemy?! Give me that!

Papa,
I'm *sorry*...
I tried
but...

SNAP

AGH!

You stomp like an *elephant*, boy.

SNAP

INNOKENTI! I know you are out here!

You leave a trail that a blind and noseless dog could follow!

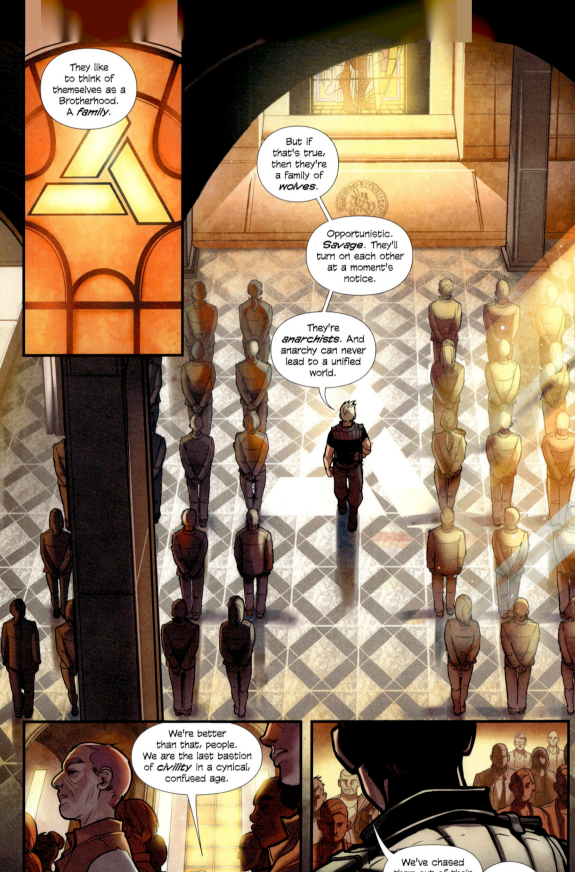

They came back from the shop today. We revised the specs according to your feedback.

Try it on, see what you think.

SHNKK

Well?

Awesome.

SNAP

PAFF

Hurgh

Hahh!

NNNFF...

HFF

Mr. Cross?

Mr. Cross?

aha.

Pardon. I wonder if you'd come with me, please.

What's up? Who are--

I would appreciate it if you would come with me, please.

Want to tell me where we're going?

Here we are.

aha.

Please let yourself in.

KLAK

From: Vidic, Warren
To: Cross, Daniel
CC:
Subject: Assignment

Our raids on the Assassin camps two years ago
unearthed a wealth of information - some
of it truly unexpected.
Thanks to your help and the element of surprise,
we discovered one of their primary server
clusters. Some of the data had been wiped,
but our analysts were able to recover a key
piece of information - the location of the
Hidden Library of Ivan the Terrible under
Moscow's Bolshoi Theater.

In and of itself, this is an incredible
discovery. Ivan Vasilyevitch (1530-
1584 - read the ref on him) collected
countless Byzantine artifacts and
texts and hid them somewhere in
the Moscow underground.

But the Assassin connection is what
interests us. We believe that generations
of Assassin leaders, including the one
they refer to as The Prophet, may have
used this library as a repository for their
records. If that is the case, anything we
find there is of incalculable strategic
importance.

Our local intel suggests that there's not much in the way of security on street level, but don't take any chances, Daniel. The simplest thing would be to attend a show. Blend in with the crowd.

ПРОШУ ПРОЩЕНИЯ.

Once inside, make your way behind the stage and into the sub-basement (see attached floor plan).

Everyone should be far too busy with the performance to notice you.

Whew.

Aaagghhhhkkkkk

Hnghh

Haah

Kaff
kaff
kaff

KK
KKK GHHGg

I'm afraid that's as much support as we can offer you, Daniel.

The recovered data gave us the location of the library, but no specifics on how to access it.

Once you're underground, look for signs of entry. Hidden doors, switches.

Feathers. They like to put feathers everywhere.

You're a resourceful young man. I know you won't let us down.

CRRRK

ТВОЮ МАТЬ!

What do we do? Go downstream and cross in the shallows?

No. The water is moving too fast and I am too slow.

We cross here.

Throw the line across to that tree.

It is young. It will hold.

CHAPTER TWO

EPILOGUE

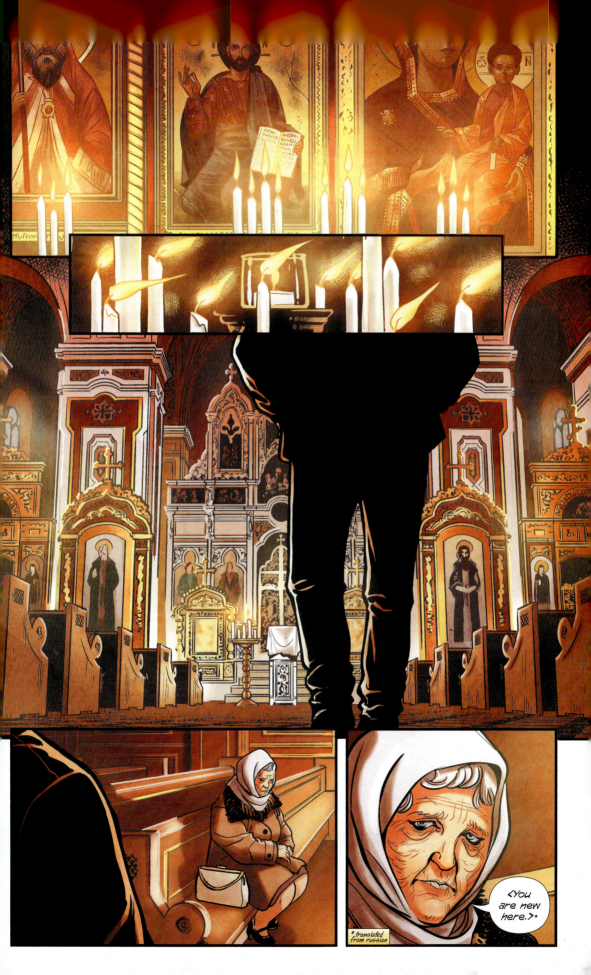

<YOU
are new
here.>*

*translated
from russian

COVER
GALLERY

The Fall issue #1 direct market

Gamestop exclusive

Target exclusive

THE FALL ISSUE #3

THE FALL ISSUE #2